Postcards
from the
Hedgehog

(*or* Some Yaks Please, I'm English.)

A.F. Harrold

First published in the UK in 2007 by

Two Rivers Press
35-39 London Street
Reading
RG1 4PS

Cover design and layout by Richard Lucas

Very Small Donkey illustration on page 43 by Linda Fraser

ISBN-13: 978 1 901677 52 2

Printed and bound by CPI Antony Rowe, Eastbourne

Acknowledgements

The Sea Slug Song was first published in a slightly different form in **Broad Street** the winners' anthology of the 1998 Reading Waterstone's Poetry Competition; *A Poem Containing An Example Of Evolution* was originally commissioned by BBC Radio 4's *The Material World*. *Very Small Donkey* was written in response to Linda Fraser's etching of the same name as part of an exhibition, some years ago, at *The Jelly Leg'd Chicken Gallery*.

Some poems first appeared, sometimes in slightly different forms, on the A.F. Harrold CDs **Revels Without Applause** (2003) *(37 Ways To Leave Your Yak; Two Yaks; The Sea Slug Song)*, **Between A Yak And A Hard Plaice** (2005) *(Plankton; The Plankton Party; A Truth About Pavements; A Poem Containing An Example Of Evolution; The Tuna's Poem; Rotten Uncle Ringo; A Busload Of Badgers; Story; The Sign Reads 'No Dogs'; a version of Cats Are Better Than Fish)*, **An Englishman's Home Is His (Modestly Priced) Third Album** (2006) *(My Name Is Diana; Poem For An Italian Friend Who Just Happens To Be A Buddhist; Polar Bears & Penguins)* and **Left Out Of The Left Field** (2006) *(13 Ways Of Looking For A Yak; Postcards From The Hedgehog; Giraffes Sitting Down; Noah's Real Story; A Scientific Investigation Into Why Snakes Fall Out Of Trees; The Camel Who Went To Sea)*.

A Brief Essay On Fruit Flies & Fainting and *The Kitchen Cow*™ were originally made available as parts of a pod-cast entitled *An Irregular Miscellany: A Collection of Lectures and Essays from the Annals of the Common University* (2006) via www.podiobooks.com. (The former is a deleted passage from the unpublished A.F. Harrold novel *The Curious Education Of Epitome Quirkstandard* (also available as an audiobook podcast from that website; the latter was a footnote from the unfinished and unpublished novel *The Life & Death Of Albert Pybus)*.)

For my mother, who helped bring me up
and who must, therefore, share some of the
responsibility for these poems.

18/2/08.

Contents

The Yak: An Invocation

Oh Yak!
  Great beast of hair and horn and hide.
Oh Yak!
  Great beast of knots and nits and noses.
Oh Yak!
  You cannot read or write or sew.
But oh Yak!
  At least you please the Nepalese.

A Poem Containing An Example Of Evolution

On an island where nut-bearing bushes prevail
a variety of birds may repose
but the ones who do best at eating the things
are the ones with the nut-cracking nose (or 'beak').

Over time it is said that their numbers increase
whilst the birds with no nuts don't survive
(if your beak won't allow you to get at the flesh
of the nut it's much harder to thrive).

And so on the island just over the way
where the hedges are covered with fruits
a different beak does the job just superb
but is rubbish at digging up roots,

which is how, on the third archipeligoed rock
we examine, the birds must eat dinner,
for the bushes round there are low, squat and bare,
and the birds, though alive, are much thinner

than the bird who inhabits the fourth island here
which it shares with cocoa and bees
and a small tribe of folk who, to fulfil the rhyme,
have slightly warped caps on their knees.

These folk take the honeycomb made by the bees
and the cocoa beans made by the shrubs
and enwrapping the former inside of the latter
make ball shaped provisions or 'grub'.

The bird of the island (you remember the bird?
we mentioned it earlier on)
is a nuisance or pest, vermin and the rest,
to the folks there who wish it were gone.

For that bird survives by violent dives
at the villagers as they're out walking
with those balls in a basket on top of their head
which is robbed by the Malteser Falcon.

Evolution suggests that the ones who do best
are simply the ones who're best-suited
to the place where they're living, that fact is a given,
and less-fitting forms simply find themselves unable to compete for
    resources and thus, in time, unless chance mutations somehow
    assist, tend to die out.

The Tuna's Poem

I bought a dolphin friendly tuna, just the other day.
I thought it'd keep my dolphin company whenever I'm away,
say out at work, or at my mum's, or maybe down the park.
I thought dolphin friendly tuna would be better than a shark.

But I hadn't counted on my dolphin, or rather I'd simply assumed too much,
for when introducing the tuna into the dolphin's hutch
the dolphin simply raised his nose as if he smelt a problem
and returned all his attention to the sardines he'd been gobbling.

The tuna was very friendly and tried to shake the dolphin's fin
and suggested games they both could play and that the dolphin ought to win
but each suggestion he suggested the dolphin dismissed without a thought,
except for one game of hide-and-seek, in which the tuna hid but the
    dolphin never sought.

The tuna got quite downcast, saying, from the place where he was hid,
'I exposed my friendliest intentions in everything I did.'
He said he'd never met a dolphin who'd made him feel so unwanted
    and so stressed
and I commiserated with him and I sold him to John West.

Fairy Tale Poem

When I was just an Ugly Duckling
I asked my mother
'What will I be?
Will I be handsome?
Will I be a swan?'
Here's what she said to me.

'No, you'll be a duck.
Just a particularly ugly one.'

What an ugly baby.

Two Yaks

Two yaks on a mountainside.
One yak says to the other yak,
'Did you hear about the Yeti?'
The other yak says,
'Bloody hell, a talking yak!'
The first yak looks at the second yak,
with a sort of ashamed look on its face and says,
'Please don't include me in this joke, I do have some dignity left.'

The Plankton Party

When I received an invitation to dinner at the house of a Blue
    Whale I know
I wasn't entirely sure whether I ought to go
because the foodstuff I had banked on
was plankton
which has never been a particular favourite of mine.
It's not that I dislike sea food, per se, I mean fish is fine,
it's just that on the other hand
plankton is rather, well shall we say, bland?

But when I arrived
I was greeted by a rather pleasant surprise:
I could have, if I wished, a bowl of krill soup
or, if I'd rather, an alternate bowl of krill cocktail.
Now, when it comes to entrée I am a soup man without fail
and so, dunking my krill bread into my krill soup I supped away
and my host pointed out the window and remarked on it being such
    a lovely day
and said, 'Why don't we adjourn to the garden?' where he'd just set up
    the barbecue.
(He'd only bought it the day before, so it was still quite new.)
He said that nothing in the summer beat the thrill of a nice krill grill,
and I was to hold nothing back and was to eat my fill,
but first he handed me a device he called a krill grill drill
because, he explained, the tiny shells of the little krill when they're
    grilled get harder still
and he began to instruct me in the correct krill grill drill skill
and because he was very safety conscious we worked through, step by
    step, the complete krill grill drill skill drill
and I had to fill in or sign an official docket or bill
using the official sea urchin inked krill grill drill skill drill bill quill.

Then he handed me some earmuffs because he explained that the
    whine of the krill grill drill is quite shrill
and it's best to be properly protected from the shrill krill grill drill trill,
although he pointed out that if you do forget your earmuffs and end
up with a headache you can always pop a shrill krill grill drill trill pill,

7

but you should be wary of this because there's nothing worse than a
    shrill krill grill drill trill pill addict
since the shrill krill grill drill trill pill addict's habit
is a hard one to fill
since the tablets are rather rare.

Then my host apologised for there being no entertainment there
and I said that I didn't mind at all a no frill krill grill
and in fact it was then my turn to apologise for in a moment of no
    frill krill grill thrill
at simply being alive at all I spilt some food on the floor,
but my host said it was alright because that's what he kept pigs for:
they were fed, it seems, on the guest's krill grill spill
which was collected up by his gardener Philip and made into a krill
    grill spill swill
and I made a little joke then and said, 'Well, I expect you call him krill
    grill spill swill Phil?'
and my host, the Blue Whale, said 'No.'

Nursery Rhyme Poem

I met a man upon the road
who looked a little like a toad
he had a broad-brimmed floppy hat
and in his arms he held a dog.

'A dog?' I said, 'That doesn't rhyme.
To carry that for all this time
is most peculiar, a dog!
No, what you want sir, is a cat.'

He looked me up and looked me down
and from the back and all around
and said, 'Sir, life is not a poem,
no, not at all, and now I'm going.'

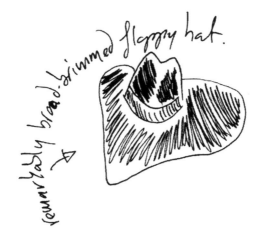

remarkably broad-brimmed floppy hat.

The Best Dessert In All Of Borneo

When you're at a dinner party in Borneo
the starters come and the starters go
but do you pay attention to them? Why, no!
They're only a prequel to the edible show.

The main course is pig or deer or shrub
or some other locally-sourced sort of grub.
By passing it over I don't mean to drub
but it's no better fare than you'd find in any pub.

So the starter's swallowed and main course's eaten,
you're sitting expectant and you see something fleetin'
from the corner of your eye (all the sheep start bleetin'):
dessert is introduced and you're pleased to be meetin'

the light fluffy ape that'll satisfy your pang
when served with fresh fruit, not fruit from a can,
or perhaps some whipped cream, or sponge or flan,
nestled beneath the bottom of the meringue-utang.

The Sign Reads 'No Dogs'

In the continent of Asia,
in the Himalayan range,
there's a one-eyed yellow idol
that the Westerners find strange

but this one-eyed yellow idol
is just a thing the natives built
to confuse intrepid white men
in their trousers or their kilts.

These white men know what happens
when a mountaineer gets lost
in the Alps or in the Andes:
Mountain Rescue send the dogs –

that bold St. Bernard breed
that's specially trained for saving people,
and although they sometimes have difficulty
if a man's stuck up a steeple

they're good at what they do
in the mountains that they know
and they're happiest when they're rollicking
with half-corpses in the snow.

But there're no dogs in the Himalayas
(though there are signs that say 'No Dogs'
(it's to do with twilight barking
simply pissing off the gods)),

so they had to find an alternative
to fill the St. Bernard's niche
and they experimented with peregrine falcons
and with mountain goats and fish.

They had a short test with a snail team
and a snake test that was rather long
and though the tiger was enthusiastic
his motivations were wrong,

and none of them showed the commitment
and none had the St. Bernard's knack
for saving missing people
that is until they tried the Yak.

The Yak liked finding people
because, it is assumed,
that once the people are out of there
the Yak has much more room

for he's a solitary creature
who does not care to share
with any living animal
the mountains that are there

and an advantage over St. Bernard
that the Yak has got, I figure,
is that the little brandy barrel
on the Yak is that much bigger.

Giraffes Sitting Down

Giraffes sit down when they want to play cards,
but they don't do it often because sitting down is hard
when your legs are as long as the giraffe's are
and when they see they've got hooves the game never gets far.

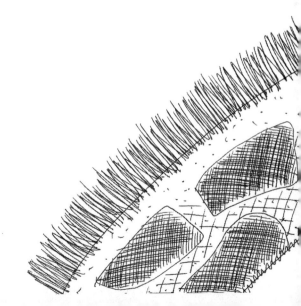

Postcards From The Hedgehog

i.
Dear Mum,

Beautiful weather.
I saw a fox last night,
did as you always said
and rolled into a ball.
After a while it went away.
I was bit scared all the same.
Wish you were here,

love Simon

ii.
Dear Mum,

Lovely weather today.
Just saw a really pretty girl.
Not sure how to approach her.
She makes me really shy
but just all warm inside.
I rolled up into a ball.
Wish you were here,

love Simon

iii.
Dear Mum,

It's raining today. I ate a slug.
Wasn't as good as the ones
you used to give us.
Tomorrow I think I'll approach the girl.
Perhaps I'll take her a slug.
She makes me ever so nervous.
I rolled up into a ball.
Wish you were here,

love Simon

iv.
Dear Mum,

Sun's come out again.
This morning I was very brave
and I went to see her.
I edged up very carefully as you suggested,
but when I spoke to her
I discovered she was actually a pine-cone.
I felt very embarrassed.
Rolled up into a ball.
Wish you were here,

love Simon

Centipede

You can't impede the scent of a centipede
anymore than a centipede can.

He's tried to wash more often,
in fact it's a personal goal,
but every time he turns on the tap
he's swept straight down the hole.

(I would draw a very
small flannel in its front
hands, but you'd never
be able to tell what it
was, so I won't.)

The Kitchen Cow™

The Kitchen Cow™ was a remarkable result of English breeding, brought about by the industrialisation and the move to urban living that reached their apogee in the nineteenth century. In the same manner as how in the countryside over centuries livestock had been bred into mountainous shapes, as full of meat as it were possible for any one animal to be, with small heads and giant shoulders and rumps, so a parallel but opposite trend was started on some forward looking city farms.

The Kitchen Cow™ stood sixteen inches high at the shoulder and had a much quieter moo than the larger members of its species. Throughout the late nineteenth century they were bought by all sorts of households to stand, as their name suggests, in the kitchen. A small pen could be bought, sat on a tabletop or counter and sown with grass and cress which the cow would eat during the day. Then, whenever necessary, a small bucket (or cup) could be placed under the swollen udders and the cow could be milked in the normal manner. In the years before refrigerators became commonplace the Kitchen Cow™ was the most convenient way of keeping milk fresh.

It was even possible to arrange a visit for your Kitchen Cow™ from the Kitchen Bull™ Man who would bring the male of the species round to your very own kitchen, settle him on top of your cow and in just a few months your herd would increase. Obviously the Kitchen Cow Company™ (KCC) insisted in strong language and with binding documentation that such offspring were strictly for personal use only and were not for resale, but equally obviously a thriving black Kitchen Cattle™ market sprang up all across the country and the KCC eventually found themselves out of business, though only a few years later, as refrigerators became more common the bottom fell out of the market altogether anyway.

The other advantage, besides free and fresh milk on tap, of a Kitchen Cow™ was that one could easily see whether to take an umbrella out before leaving the house by checking whether the Kitchen Cow™ was lying down in her little field or not.

Four Ways Of Looking At A Yak

after Wallace Stevens

i.

Among twenty snowcapped mountains
nothing moves except
the jaw of the yak.

ii.

I was very worried,
like a tree
in which there perches a solitary yak.

iii.

A man and a woman
are one.
A man and a woman and a yak
are one
and a man and a woman.

iv.

It is clear that there are only
two
states of existence – Yak and Non-Yak.

Dugongs and Manatees

All I get now is grief from my Dugong.
All I hear are his moaning complaints.
For ages I thought we were friends, you know,
but friends is the one thing we ain't.

We no longer spend much time together.
By night we are not skinny-dippers.
Not since he got drunk on some strong orange squash
from a hip flask he held in his flippers.

He'd tell me, he said, about my new friend,
but, you see, Dugongs don't do subtlety,
and it was moan, moan, moan, and excessively clear
that the dugong was jealous of me,
         of me and my Manatee.

For my Manatee is marvellous, he's mighty and mysterious,
a merry-making, mussel-munching mugwump or sampan.
He masticates, while maundering, marmite spread with marjoram
on marrows from the marketplace and muffins from the man.

My Manatee will manducate like a maniac on maple leaves;
on mangrove roots his mandibles will more than often munch.
His malaprops are mythical. His merchandise is marginal
and mainly made in Malay and mainly made of mops.

My Manatee's immaculate, his madrigals are memorable,
he manipulates marimbas but he mimes the Marseillaise.
He is mates with master muezzins and many minor mandarins
and myrmidons and majorettes and Maharajah's maids.

My Manatee's met Mexicans, Margravines and matadors,
motorists and moralists and mordacious mountebanks,
maidens and Mohammedans, Mafiosi, Machiavellians,
a mayor, a monk, melungeons and moggies (mainly Manx).

Now the Dugong just dawdles so desperately
wherever my Manatee and I process,
and he pretends he's not there and, well, so do we.
It's such a duffer, a Dugong depressed.

My Manatee mouth-to-mouthed a mountaineer, when Medevac were
nowhere near.
His menagerie is mellifluous with marmosets and mice,
mooses and marsupials, mink, moles, muntjacs, mandrills
and in marshy mazes all around the Manatee grows rice.

He mixes macadamia in and makes it into macaroons
and magpie pie and marzipan and mandrake cake and mince.
His muesli's manly, meaty mix is measured out in ceramics
which maximise the median and make the meal immense.

Oh! my Manatee's a mariner, unmissable he's manifest,
he's a martinet when military matters are displayed.
He's mercurial with merchantmen and mermaids, and with money-men
he's a mean and moody monster whenever menaces are made.

My Manatee plays mummeries with matriarchs from nunneries
he murmurs and he mumbles; mutilates the masquerade.
But there's no malice in his mucilage and moving pictures by and large
who manage mucronating their motifs may still get made.

But the Dugong drifts by in a dinghy
not looking either of us in the eye,
and I feel a short twinge of resentment
as I wish that that Dugong would die.

But now my Manatee has a malady, which mainly means morbidity:
his millet's turned to meerschaum, his malamute's turned to milk.
His malversation is all malmsey, he demands his mummy's mammary.
Is this malaria or Malarmé or merely too much Liebfraumilch?

My Manatee has a malison, it's malign and not malingering;
the markings, unmistakable, are minacious in the maximum,
malicious and impendingly, mind-numbingly grim and ominous...

Oh, how the sea-cow mews a final meek and minute moo.

So my Manatee's mortal in the end, and all I wanted was a friend,
to make me feel a little needed. Oh, a Dugong will have to do.

37 Ways To Leave Your Yak

You can leave it as left luggage at Fulham Broadway Station.
You can leave it in your will as a gift for all the nation.
You can wrap it up in paper for an elderly relation.
Or send it back to Amazon as a customer cancellation.

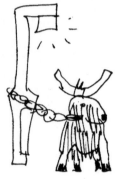

You can chain it to a lamp post with the
    appropriate length of chain.
You can flush it down the toilet; you can push it
    from the train.
Buy a one way ticket on a package tour to Spain.
Or bake it in a cake and then leave it in the rain.

You can leave your Yak in France,
you can leave it at a dance,
you can lose your Yak in poker if you think you
    have a chance.

You can join the Yak's Trade Union and force the Yak
    to picket.
Creep into Lord's late at night, disguise it as a wicket.
Buy an arsenic lollipop, entice the Yak to lick it.
You can leave it high, leave it dry or lose it in a thicket.

You can leave your Yak a broken Yak, all twisted up
    and bitter.
Call Rent-o-Kill to come and deal with a great big hairy critter.
Report it to the authorities for the dropping, say, of litter
and when your Yak tells you he's going to prison just say, 'Really?
    What a bummer.'

You can give your Yak to God.
You can batter it like cod.
You can call yourself a rocker and declare your Yak a mod.

You can feed your Yak Brussels sprouts and very soon he'll leave you.
Fake your death or suicide, the Yak's bound to believe you.
Bury him in the orchard, then sit back, admire the tree view.
You can get your Yak press-ganged in Portsmouth for the heave to.

You can turn your Yak to pasta, sarnie, pie
    or quiche or strudel.
You must shave your Yak carefully to
    prepare the big bamboozle:
go to Crufts (when Crufts is on), pretend
    your Yak's a poodle
and if they question your dog's pedigree explain
    it with an ingenious paper napkin doodle.

You can leave your Yak at
    home.
You can leave it on its own.
You can leave it like a coward with a message on
    the phone.

Now why would I want to leave the Yak? Am I just
    a nutter?
A Yak's not bad, they're big and strong, make milk
    and cheese and butter.
They're horny and quite beautiful when eyelashes start to flutter
but although I speak quite clearly the Yak don't hear a word I utter.

He's deaf to all suggestions of things *I* would like to do.
Every weekend it's just the same, we end up at the zoo
and then it's down to Joshi's for a veggie vindaloo
and no Yak is pleasant company when that lot passes through.

A Truth About Pavements

It's best to be wary of pavements,
sometimes they creep up on you
with their crablike shuffle,
their sideways walk,
and they slip their kerb away from
or unexpectedly under
your feet or foot,
causing you to trip up, slip, misstep
or otherwise blunder your way
into embarrassment.
Although it's hard to be sure of their motives
I suspect pavements are probably just perniciously puckish.

My Maiden Plant

My pot plant's the only virgin in the flat.
She's shy and always blushes tenderly
when someone mentions the bumblebee.

Autumn

In the autumn of the year
only two things are clear,
the facts are these:
the leaves leave the trees;
except for the evergreens
who leave their leaves in their eaves.

My Name Is Diana

Well, I'm a giraffe.
Please do not laugh.

I live on the savannah.
My name is Diana.

I like to eat leaves
from acacia trees.

I'm up to eighteen feet tall.
Have between two and five horns.

I've got prehensile lips
and very high hips.

I'm chestnut on pale buff.
My tail ends in a tuft.

My eye's large and lustrous.
My tongue is quite dextrous.

Because I'm so tall
I've seen it all:

I've watched cheetahs cheating;
seen elephants meeting;

watched antelope lope;
I once met the Pope.

I'm afraid that's a lie.
It was some other guy.

13 Ways Of Looking For A Yak

One way to meet a Yak is with a small ad
advertising various sorts of gorse,
or you could hire a detective to try to track one down
but don't attempt to hire Inspector Morse,
because he's not a detective of the freelance sort
and he's dead, and he's fictional of course.

You can check every so often outside your front door
to see if one is sitting on the mat,
or you can squat in the kitchen with a torch through the night
to see if one is brought in by the cat,
but do ensure you've a list of distinguishing features
to distinguish it from bird and frog and rat.

You could take a bent hairpin in your pocket to the zoo
and wiggle it about in all the locks,
or you could go on the rampage in John Lewis and request
an address for the suppliers of their range of Yak-hair socks.

If you hang around the supermarket checkouts
ask each Yak if he needs help to pack his bag:
you might find one less proud than all the others,
who'll admit that sometimes hooves can be a drag
but the sort of Yak who'd admit that to a stranger
is the sort of Yak who's probably a danger:
not just insanely jealous, but afraid of umbrellas
and liable to eat all your hydrangea.

You could travel quite a lot on all the railways
because it's a noted fact that Yaks rarely fly,
although just to be firmly on the safe side
best keep a weather eye out on the sky,
and also you should hang around the graveyard,
even Yaks, it is said, must sometimes die.

In a library, where everyone else is quiet,
you could follow the sound of a low and mournful lowing,
although be warned some sounds can be misleading
and you might just find a Wildebeest who's going
to the toilet in a most importunate setting,
for a Wildebeest is happiest when he's flowing.

Best not to mix too much with the Wildebeest
they've never much been fans of house-training.
Although if you find you must date one (in extremis),
then best do it in the park, when it is raining.

But you're going to find a Yak wherever Wildebeest are not
because the two things are really rather diametric
and you'll also find the Yak where things are very calm
because they do not like the world to be too hectic
and, importantly, don't forget to not visit the LSE
'cause no Yak spends time discussing dialectic.

And do remember that Yaks are not at all gregarious
you won't ever see them hung around in groups,
or in the bath, in a belfry or a bookshop,
or disguised as the comedian Greg Proops.

And one final tip I feel is necessary
to leave you with before I must be going
if you don't mind finding where to find a second-hand Yak
then pay attention when I read **the other poem**.

Plankton

Some plankton I know
had difficulty getting to sleep at night,
went out and bought a relaxation tape –
Pacific Whale Song.

Didn't help much.

A Bedouin Proverb

Watch out where the camels stand
and don't you eat that yellow sand.

Zoological Song

All monotremes have a cloaca,
which is one little hole in the end.

The Platypus and the Echidna
are the monotremes I recommend.

Instead of urethra and anus,
the cloaca functions as both,

'Only one way out,' is the motto
that serves as the monotreme's oath.

Your wee and your eggs and your pooh-pooh
(or if you're a man then your sperm)

all use the same singular channel.
As to which comes when you just learn.

The Mouse's Mistake

On the day that the mouse ate the elephant
we were all somewhat surprised
in part 'cause we'd fed the mouse earlier
and in part for the difference in size.

When questioned the mouse explained
that he'd been bet by a man that he knew
and a fiver's a fiver he carelessly shrugged
and an elephant makes a good stew.

But that elephant, I tried to explain to him,
was our friend and our pet and on loan
from the zoo in Bristol who'd kindly allowed
him a weekend away for a roam.

When the weekend was up and we had to return
that elephant back to the zoo
we tied the hoover hose onto his nose
and hoped that the mouse would do.

The Camel Who Went To Sea *(a song)*

I had lived all my life as a ship of the desert
   with a man sat high on my back,
and I admit though the weather was often quite pleasant
   I didn't care much about that,
for a daydreaming camel I happened to be,
and the desert was never the right place for me,
for I'd seen a magazine
   and read there a letter
which told of a life
   clearly much better,
so I forsook my friends and I gave them the hump
and I ran away to sea.

I stowed away on a schooner, which was bound for China,
   which I hoped would never sail back,
in Marakesh I jumped ship and embarked on a liner
   with a tall salt-caked smokestack.
I hid in a lifeboat for most of the day
and listened to all that the crewmen would say,
they talked about biscuits
   and also the weather
and the rotten old captain
   who beat them whenever
he felt they'd transgressed, so I gave him the hump
and dumped the old man in the sea.

At first all the sailors were rather unsure
   about what I'd done to their maniacal captain
they threatened to dump me on some foreign shore:
   the bosun attempted but sadly got trapped in
the hold and was heard from no more.

The sailors soon realised which side they were buttered
   and we have no more talk of their treacherous mutiny.
My cabin has portholes most wonderfully shuttered.
   To save me from scurvy I get lots of fruit in me.

So I live out my life as a ship of the sea now
    as a pirate of worthy renown,
Blackbeard and Bluebeard are both scared of me now
    'cause I wear the pirate king's crown,
for I've an advantage in pirateous deeds:
my ship and myself lack certain needs,
all ships that you've seen
    you'd swear that they oughta
be incapable of travelling
    outside of the water
but we go seven days with the aid of my hump,
    a whole week without any sea.

We've robbed the crown jewels from the Tower Of London,
we sailed right in and right out without stopping,
Fort Knox and Great Trains we've cruised alongside,
we've taken the veil from a very pale bride,
Ratners we plundered in towns north and south,
stolen false teeth from pensioners' mouths,
we're pirates who spit when sailors we thump,
down in the bilges we pump and we pump,
we cuss and we swear and we fight one another,
at the end of the day, though, I still love my mother,
    I pop in and tell her my tales over tea
    for I am the camel who went to sea,
    I'm the camel who went to sea, I am,
    I'm the camel who went to sea.

Some Reasons Why Cats Are Better Than Fish

Nobody ever says 'It's a fish eat cat world.'

A cat can eat its dinner from a dish.
What animal can't do that? A Fish.

Fish have fins and cats have paws.
Fins may be fine but they can't do doors.

'According to Charles Darwin's Theory of Evolution by Natural Selection
    a cat is simply a fish with 300 million years worth of improvements.'

Cats can swim **and** walk on land
put a fish on the shore and it can't even stand.

A tiger is a cat that likes to swim
put a shark on the land and it won't do a thing.

If a shark stops for a moment the shark will start to sink
but a cat can stop for as long as it likes and have a lovely think.

One proverbially measures a room with a cat
but in no axiom at all does a fish do that.

'The Ancient Egyptians revered cats; none of their gods had the head
    of a hake.'

You can cuddle a cat but
would you hug a halibut?

Rubbish Animal.

Thin Cat on Rug.

Good animals.

Noah's Song

It was a bit of a shame and was a touch awkward
that Noah was allergic to the cats and to the birds.

He sneezed when in his cabin, his eyes streamed on the deck,
but surrounded by those animals he just said 'Flipping heck,

I have a pair of everything, including viruses and bugs.'
And Mrs Noah turned to him and gave a little hug

but as she drew him closer, he sniffed and sneezed once more
and she took a breath and closed her eyes and fainted to the floor

because Noah had been working hard clearing the elephant's dung
and the baboons' and the oxen's, mucking out one by one

and a little bit of every stool still lingered in the air
around his splattered work clothes, on his cheek and in his hair.

Ham and Shem, Noah's sons, carried Mrs Noah away,
and Noah grew more upset because upon the day

when he first designed the Ark and when God approved the plan
he hadn't thought about a bathroom and then the rain began.

He'd quickly knocked together a most amazing boat
that could carry two of everything and always stay afloat

but space was of course restrictive and sanitation low on his list
and there was a wonderful tiller but the shower just got missed.

So he sneezes and a tear falls. A rhino walks the deck.
A spider crawls up his shoulder and into his turtleneck.

'No shower,' he swears quite loudly as he walks through the snooker hall
past the miniature golf and the library and the modernised shopping mall.

'No shower,' he swears at the Steinway in the music room (second class),
and he thinks to himself that given time the mucking out smell will pass

but not very quickly and not very well without artificial help
and he can hear that it's still raining and he gives a little yelp;

this is the second day in the Ark and there'd be at least thirty-eight more
and Noah knows Mrs Noah right down to the tone of her snore

and he knows she won't let him kiss her as long as he smells like a pooh
and he'll be sleeping somewhere with the animals, as smelly folks tend to.

So the moral of this cautionary tale is clear to you and me
make sure you adequately design the sanitation services you plan to
    provide before you go to sea.

Story

I was in a woman's bedroom once and I noticed on her shelf a tarantula, but when I got closer I noticed that it was made out of an old washing up bottle and some pipe cleaners. Then I saw a bat hanging in the corner, or rather what I took to be a bat, in actual fact it was an old umbrella painted to look like a bat with a bit of Astroturf for a body. Then I went to sit on her bed but stopped short because there was a big tabby cat asleep on it already, although when I looked closer it turned out to be a bit of sticky-backed plastic and a couple of cotton reels. So I remained where I stood and spoke to the woman whose room it was about the value of truth and trust in a relationship and I was heartbroken when she admitted that all along she'd been faking organisms.

Rotten Uncle Ringo

Uncle Ringo
and his dingo
often went to bingo halls

and stole the balls.

One Way To Leave Your Yam

Just put it down and walk away
(you'll live to see another day).

A Poem For An Italian Friend Who Happens To Be A Buddhist
(after T.S. Eliot)

Macavity's a mystery Yak, he's called the hidden hoof.
He's bovine Zen Master who has seen the eight-fold truth.
He's the burden of the Buddhists, the Dalai Lama's worst despair,
for when they reach Nirvana, well, Macavity's not there.

The Yak attempts the Lotus position...

Very Small Donkey

(after an etching of the same name by Linda Fraser.)

Let's get two things straight right at the beginning.

Firstly, there are no optical illusions here, no tricks of perspective, no sleight of hand. This Donkey is in fact Very Small.

And secondly, there are no metaphors here, no sly allusions or hidden meanings. This Very Small Donkey really is just a Donkey.

Sometimes the Very Small Donkey wakes in a cold sweat in the middle of the night, one hoof clutching to its chest, eyes staring into the darkness, the horror of its nightmare imprinted onto the backs of its eyelids. There is only one thing that this Very Small Donkey fears and it is that, unseen, the end nears. For when one is so very small one sometimes has difficulty being noticed by larger beings at all. Shouting out a warning has no effect. And it can be difficult to outrun or dodge, for instance, the sole of a shoe. This is the Very Small Donkey's nightmare, it is always different and it is always the same...

> The foot of a man descends from above,
> the foot of a ram, the beak of a dove,
> the hoof of a goat, the paw of a cat,
> the foot of a toad, the foot of a rat,
> the foot of a dog, the foot of a rook,
> the foot of a frog, the slam of a book,
> the nibble of mice, the flatfooted goose,
> the insidious lice, the lumberjacked spruce,
> the caw of a crow, Honoré de Balzac,
> herons and horses and gerbils and yak,
> the talons of pelicans, eagles or owls,
> robins and magpies and various fowls,
> the steal of the stoat, the grunt of a pig
> (to be eaten by that would just be *infra dig*),
> to be chewed with the cud, to be threshed with the wheat,
> to be eaten by starlings or swans or a sheep,
> the glint of a vole, the wink of the fox,

to be scraped from the sole of some juvenile's socks,
the foot of an elephant, hippo or rhino
impressing this Donkey into the lino,
the opossum or aardvark or lump of Gruyère,
the paw of the polar or grizzly bear,
the foot of a penguin, or if it's hotter
the foot of an antelope, ermine or otter,
a duck, other donkeys, asses and mules,
albatross, guinea fowl or gallinules,
to be smothered by slugs or (just better) snails,
to be swallowed and filtered by squadrons of whales,
the paw of a lion, the paw of a tiger,
the jaw of the lynx, the hoof of a saiga,
caribou, reindeer, elk, moose or boar
pay little attention to what's on the floor
or what's underfoot, unless it's a truffle
or acorn or roughage or mushroom to snuffle,
being crushed into dust by George Bernard Shaw,
out walking whilst talking to Evelyn Waugh
about certain dimensions of Zsa Zsa Gabor,
is not, if you think, what living is for
but still more images flit in this dream
of kangaroos bouncing on through the scene,
then the sniff of a badger just out of its set,
or it trips in the path of the last suffragette
and it dreams that it hears as it's took to the vet
the voice of some Princess who whispers 'Not yet, Sweet Donkey
          don't die, not yet.'

And the Very Small Donkey lies woken in its barn and looks
towards the rising sun which wearily warms the rafters, its breathing
returning to normal after the sudden shock of waking and it thinks
to itself being small has its ups and downs but, after all, love can
conquer all divides and one day, perhaps soon, it will be this Very
Small Donkey's turn to shine.

(actual size)

Noah's Real Story

My neighbour has had a dream.
I overheard him telling Mrs Jones,
who lives on the other side, all about it.

In it he received instructions
detailing the proportions
and the method of construction
required for a great big boat.

Since we live some distance from the coast
and since it is for the most part a dry land
I paid him and his dream little heed.

But Mrs Jones (who is a widow) didn't.
In fact she positively encouraged him.

Day by day crossing their two gardens
grew the spine and ribs of a great big boat.
They covered it, tarred it and three weeks later
they broke a bottle of champagne on it.

They invited the whole neighbourhood round.

We had a guided tour and it all looked very nice.
Mr. Peterson, from number fourteen,
began to feel seasick and had to be helped off.
My boys walked him home. Very kind, I thought.

The next morning everyone woke up
to the sound of something alien in the garden
and on the roofs.

What had begun as a sprinkling became a downpour.
When young Shem came back from the newsagent
my *Daily Telegraph* was simply pulp.
It was raining that hard.

Outside the back window a row of shapes was passing.
Giraffe, cobra, gnu, chinchilla, marmoset, puma,
caribou, coypu, apricot, antelope, kangaroo,
panther, wolf, bison, ocelot, bear, sheep, dog and frog.

I stuck my head out and shouted at my neighbour,
'What's all this then?' 'Animals,' he replied.
'On my flowerbeds,' I said, 'They're ruined.'
He clearly didn't hear as he continued counting.

I gathered the boys up to go over there
in order to discuss my flowerbeds man to man.

By the time I'd found my waterproof sandals,
fastened my biggest robe around me and set out
he'd counted the last of his menagerie aboard.
I stormed up the gangplank to make my point.

'Hello neighbour,' he said benevolently,
obviously misunderstanding the look on my face.
'There's not much room left after the animals,
but me and Mrs Jones don't mind squeezing up.'

'My flowerbeds,' I roared above the increasing rain,
'They're absolutely ruined. Trampled, eaten, crushed.'

'Oh dear,' he said, 'I didn't realise. I'll see what I can do,'
and so he set off down the gangplank, trowel in hand,
'You just keep an eye on the animals for me,
make sure they don't get into any more mischief.'

So me and the boys kept an eye on the animals
while the thunder continued to crash.
After a while, and a short game of cards, I stood up.
And as I stood up I wobbled. The whole room wobbled.

Outside the gangplank was drifting away towards the houses.
And all that remained to be seen of the houses was their roofs.
And very soon all that remained of the roofs was the aerials.
And I turned to the boys and said, 'Has anyone seen Mrs Jones.'

Polar Bears & Penguins

The polar bears over there
care for their hare
(a rabbit like thing they've adopted).
They feed it pear slices
and also fresh air,
and the thing that's most nice is
they comb the hare's hair
and they pick it out outfits
the hare will then wear
to the parties it's chosen or opted
to go to.

The penguins are jealous because
they've never received the polar bears' love
'But that's not surprising,' the polar bears say,
'Penguins are not often seen round our way,
but if they were we'd be happy to welcome them in
it takes a long time for our friendship to thin,
and there's always sardines when we open the tin.'

But the hare gets all uppish
and lowers his ears
which is how a hare displays his fears
when he hears
conversations like these,
since the hare's always near
to plunging despair
and is easy to scare
in the polar bears' lair
with the thought that their love
he might soon have to share,
and the bears might compare
his ears and his hair in a way most unfair
to the penguin's smart flair.
Oh! it's all a nightmare.

Parrots Are Not To Be Confused With Dogs

A few tips.

If you take a parrot for a walk there's one thing you'll need
and that's a very long lead
because parrots tend to fly
higher in the sky
than dogs do.

And when you throw a stick
the parrot may well perch on it
and if you shout 'Fetch'
bear in mind that the parrot's the only pet
equipped to quip, 'Fetch it yourself, buster.'

A Busload Of Badgers

The collective noun for badgers is a *busload,*
the collective term for foxes is a *wig,*
a massing crowd of monkeys is a *teapot,*
and caterpillars cluster in a *gig.*

More than one kangaroo's a *landfill,*
two or more elephants is a *sack,*
crows move in *books,* as do sealions and rooks,
but a yak is just a yak is just a yak.

The collective noun for lions is a *desktop,*
the collective term for sheepdogs is a *hump,*
the word for massed magpies is a *front room,*
and a group of elk or moose is a *dump.*

Even tigers come together in a *plectrum,*
a group of cheetahs you would call a *deck* or *pack,*
and we all know it's a *slaughter* of rabbits,
but a yak is just a yak is just a yak.

A yak doesn't go much for company,
he doesn't *flock* or *muster, herd* or *pod,*
he prefers the single life, makes do without a wife
and needs a collective noun as much as God.

That's as much as God needs a description
to be used when there are several Gods around,
although in Ancient Greece and in the Hindu lands, at least,
the use for such a term is quickly found.

And so the same could be said about a Yak too
(not that the Hindus or the Greeks need a word
to express what they see when a Yak turns up with three
other Yaks – that would just be absurd;

it's not restricted in that way to those peoples,
but all the peoples, everywhere, everyday
may well find they need the word, that's so very rarely heard
because it's the sort of word that people just don't say very often).

But because it's rarely said perhaps, or never,
it's not a collective noun that's widely known,
(and I know that's tautologic but that means it's faultless logic)
and so I decided to do some research of my own.

I went and asked a Himalayan goatherd,
since if anybody'd know he'd be the chap,
but since I don't speak Nepalese or Tibetan or Chinese
it really didn't help very much.

The Sea Slug Song

You've heard the talk of dolphins
and of how beautiful they are.
You've heard the talk of whales and squids
and manta rays and sharks
and you've seen the tiny plankton
and the sea horses and stuff
and heard Cousteau go on about them all
'cause he just can't get enough

of all the lovely creatures
what inhabit the seven seas,
but there's one he may have mentioned
(but which he never mentioned to me)
that you rarely read a record of
in the Sunday magazines
but I saw it in an old picture book
and it was the creature of my dreams...

The sea slug.
The glorious sea slug.
She's a creature that has quite thrilling external gills.

The sea slug.
The marvellous sea slug.
Whenever I see her breathing it always gives me chills.

Just imagine Nicole Kidman
when she has no arms or legs.
No nose, no ears, no eyes, no hair –
just lying there in bed.
Now, imagine the bed's all sandy
and that she's about six inches long
and that her skin is opalescent
and shiny and worthy of song...

And that's the sea slug.
The beautiful sea slug.
The sea slug is the slug that I like to see.

The sea slug.
The fabulous sea slug.
If I'm ever reincarnated it's the sea slug for me.

She's as lithe as any tiger
what roams through India.
She's cuter than Bridget Bardot
in or out her underwear.
She's smarter and she's prettier
than Johnny Ball and daughter
and what is even better
she can breathe when underwater...

   'Cause she's the sea slug.
   The glorious sea slug.
   The sea slug's the most dazzling slug you've ever seen.

   The sea slug.
   The wonderful sea slug.
   She's a truly subaqueous nudibranchial queen.

Now, you can see why I love the sea slug,
why the sea slug fills my dreams
with an extra-speciel longing
that defies my brilliant schemes
'cause no matter how hard I work at it
she'll never accept my hand
because I don't look good in a diving suit
and she doesn't look good on land...

   'Cause she's a sea slug.
   The fantastical sea slug.
   And I'll never stop dreaming of what might have been –

   if I was a sea slug.
   And she was a sea slug.
   Together in a lucid wet Neptunian dream.

Bear Song

When I grow up I want to be a bear,
I'm working on the stoop and I'm working on the hair
and I'm working on the paunch and I'm working on the stare,
when I grow up I want to be a bear.

When I grow up I want to hibernate,
I'll go to bed early, get out of bed late,
wouldn't worry about the time – simply note the date,
when I grow up I want to hibernate.

William's Song

Everybody stares at William's wings
(those two glorious and upraised things.)
They sprout from his shoulders into the air
and whichever way he turns they are always there
and they're colourful, yes, they're coloured like light
and when the sun catches them they're ever so bright.

He sits in the morning on his windowsill,
he stretches for a moment and then he is still.
The sun warms the blood that runs in his wings
(those two glorious and upraised things)
and when they're awake he'll fly into school
but he walks in the corridor 'cause that is the rule.

And William's a brave boy, never afraid
of lions or tigers from a circus parade
or an owl that might eat children up with a snap
'cause William has defences displayed on his back,
two giant eyes, one on each of his wings
(those two glorious and upraised things.)

Jim & The Lion: A Cautionary Tale
(obviously after both Marriott Edgar and Hilaire Belloc)

Boys who choose to visit zoos
should tie the laces of their shoes
or if one's handy find a grown-up
to ensure their shoes are neatly sewn up,

for flapping laces, it has been said,
can lead to children being dead.
Take for instance little Jim
it was loose laces that did for him.

In the zoo he yelled and ran around
excited by all the things he'd found:
wolves and bears and snakes and rats
and leopards, tigers and other cats

of a large and toothy look
that Jim had read about in his book.
He ran toward the lion's pen,
his shoelace flapped, he tripped and then

he flew face first towards the cage
with a shout (not calm and sage)
and with a pop his head slid through
the cage's bars and stuck like glue.

His parents tugged at Jimmy's feet
but each tug they tugged met with defeat.
His ears were blocking his retreat
and so it was Jim became meat.

For the noise Jim made, all his crying,
had woken up the sleeping lion
who slowly walked up to the lad,
then looked up at Jim's mum and dad.

The lion saw how Jim was stuck
between the bars by rotten luck.
Those two big ears, they were the problem
and so the lion started gobbling.

But a lion's not a tidy eater,
as eaters go you're probably neater,
but a lion always eats the lot
and never leaves any of what he's got.

Jim's parents couldn't blame the lion
for eating Jim, they were always trying
to teach the boy in many places
not to run with undone laces.

A Brief Essay On Fruit Flies & Fainting

For a long time it was simply assumed that the act of fainting was caused by a complex interaction between environmental, medical and emotional factors, but a Viennese researcher attempted to investigate these unfounded assumptions once and for all in a series of experiments conducted just before the First World War.

Arthur Fraudengold spent three years in a laboratory attempting to induce fainting in fruit flies. For three years he was entirely unsuccessful, except for one unrepeated incident that happened late on a Friday afternoon. For this particular experiment he had raised the humidity in the fruit fly box (where they lived under strictly controlled conditions) and whispered some shocking news (about a new insecticide he'd read about in *The Viennese Scientists' Weekly Round-Up*) down the special whispering tube that was the only link between their two environments. As he watched through the toughened glass one of the fruit flies, Matilda, spiralled down towards the floor. Just before she impacted, however, with the soiled newspapers he kept there for safekeeping she regained control of her wings and fluttered in her flyish way back up to some fruit that lay on a high shelf.

Fraudengold noted this event in his journal with undisguised disgust. Over the previous few years he had come to admire the fruit fly for its assiduous failure to faint. He had convinced himself that he had found an animal that had raised itself above all the petty self-importance and fatuous self-loathing that so ensnared and plagued his own species, that made them so weak and so prone to collapsing in heaps on the ground at the slightest provocation. But he knew what he had seen Matilda do and never forgave that fly for blotting the copy-book of her otherwise flawless family.

In August 1915 Arthur Fraudengold was married. His bride to be was the daughter of a wealthy Austrian industrialist and wrote a weekly column in a powerful national newspaper. She had graduated a year earlier from two respected universities simultaneously and was the second youngest artist to have a picture hung in the foyer of the Vatican. Arthur was mad about her, she was his intellectual match and when he looked in her vertiginous brown eyes he saw a long and vigorous home life spinning out ahead of him for years to come.

Mmm, this is a tasty little cake.

However, he worried that the heat in the church and the excitement of the day and all the standing up, might be her undoing. That August was, of course, particularly hot and he had observed that, at weddings he had been at before, it sometimes happened that the bride, or a bridesmaid, would collapse in the aisle or apse waving a small paper fan before her face and looking human, all too human.

To forestall such an eventuality, which would destroy the deep respect and love he felt for her, he asked his wife-to-be to stay at home during the ceremony. She agreed and on the day her dress and role was filled and fulfilled by a plump little fruit fly called Fiona. Arthur had absolute faith in her not fainting. Some of the groom's friends and family, who had not met the bride before the wedding, looked on at the spectacle with a mixture of disgust, schadenfreude and confusion lapping across their faces. The bride's half of the church was pale and quiet, although an occasional buzzing wafted up from the pews.

Everything went well at the ceremony: Fiona said, on behalf of the industrialist's daughter, in her tiny voice, 'I do,' and then she sat symbolically inside the bride's ring. It was only a little later, when it came to signing the register, that any difficulties occurred. In all the excitement of the moment Fiona became confused and signed her own name instead of that of the industrialist's daughter, as had been planned, and so Arthur was legally bound, in wedlock, to a *Drosophila melanogaster* or fruit fly. 'It's surprising,' he wrote in his diary that evening, 'That something like this doesn't happen more often.'

Understanding that the law is the law, and that to set oneself above it or in opposition to it was to invite anarchy to rule the world, Arthur carried on his duty as husband without displaying a qualm.

There was some malicious talk amongst the guests at the reception when the bride vomited on her piece of cake, but it was generally agreed a tragic waste of a young life when she flew, a little tipsy perhaps, into a spider's web just before she and Arthur were due to have their first dance.

Before anyone could move to rescue her she was violently, and wholly, consumed by the owner of the web. This put a dampener on the party and Arthur sent everyone home, sweeping the hall himself, sadly, in the darkness.

After an appropriate period of mourning the widower, Arthur, married his original intended bride. In a much appreciated gesture he suggested that any guests who had brought a present to the previous marriage would need only bring a small token present to this second wedding.

At the reception, in a tragic and ironic twist that provoked a mixture of laughter and tears from the room, the industrialist's daughter suffered exactly the same fate, in the same cobweb, again just before the first dance, that Fiona had a week before.

Scientific Investigations Into Why Snakes Fall Out Of Trees

It's dangerous in the jungle as you're walking through the shrubs:
in your hand-sewn khaki shorts you're just another source of grub
to all the jaguars and spiders and the pitcher plants and mice,
and missionaries gone native with the anthrophogaic vice.

But the biggest difficulty I encountered or had to take
was the constant susurration and thudding of falling snakes.
You can't move two yards in the jungle without one falling on your head
and it wouldn't be such a bother if the buggers fell down dead

but they're always wriggling and writhing and twisting all around
and constantly exhibiting a sort of hissing snake-ish sound
and it's really all rather unnerving and it gives a man the willies
but there's a much more serious problem (and it doesn't rhyme
    with 'willies'):

for concussion stalks the explorer who removes his hat or helmet;
for example, when meeting a lady explorer one always bows and says
    'Well met,
madam,' and removes the aforesaid headgear in a gesture renowned
    as a tip,
and Sod's Law says quite simply *that's* when plummeting snakes will hit.

So exploring becomes a question, tossing between impolitic actions,
breaches of etiquette abound on each side and explorers are split
    into factions:
there's the tippers, non-tippers, bruised and unharmed,
 the snubbers and cutters, the politely abashed,
the haughty, the proud, the egregious and dumb,
 and those who go nowhere a cheque can't be cashed.

But to return to the question of plummeting snakes
I've done much more research than it's usual to make
and I've reached some conclusions that were published in Nature:
a highly respected journal, but if you don't take it, I won't hate you

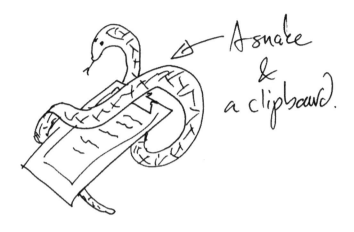

A snake
&
a clipboard.

because there are magazines I don't have time to read
and if you publish in them then I hope to not plead
with you to forgive me for not scanning your entry
for my time is filled up like that of a sentry

with standing quite still and in silence and jungles
and noting the facts that I spot of the bungles
of snakes in the branches who fall to the floor
and I note on my clipboard with a pencil a score

of distinguishing features that inhere in the snakes
who collapse to the ground when the slightest wind shakes
the limb of a tree and I draw me a graph
to prove my results then I signal my staff

to cable my findings off to the editor
(my staff's a fine lass and I did hope to credit her
by naming a snake or a land snail or spider
but sadly my wife disapproved of the idea).

So I'll give you a précis, or failing that a synopsis,
of what I noted whilst lurking below ampelopsis
(that's a tropical vine beneath which I was hid;
if you ask did I do that? I'll say, 'Yes, I did,'

because not being observed is a scientist's aim:
to all observed observers I say 'Do it again,'
for their observations are wishful and scanty
and corrupted and rancid and frankly I'm anti

all such non-scientists but back to the snakes...)
...I spent seventeen years and I made some mistakes
but I soon isolated the singular reason
that holds for all snakes regardless of season

or gender or age or colour or learning
or amount that the snake could be thought to be earning
when equating the scale of its labour to wages
in comparable rôles here in England and pages

of charts so complex I filled up with my ink
and notebooks were stuffed with the stuff I would think
and it all was distilled in one sentence of words
that solved the conundrum: 'Snakes are not birds.'

But more than this holds, there are other key facts,
for example, subsidiary: 'Snakes are not bats,'
but that's only to say the conclusion I spy
encloses both statements: 'Snakes cannot fly.'

Science is purest when simplest, they say,
but I'll add one conclusion to the rest, if I may,
and that is to note with rigour and candour
that further to this: 'A snake is not a panda.'

And this list could go on, I've drawn many conclusions
and dashed, I should hope, a whole host of illusions
that folks who've not studied the snake quite so closely
might make to themselves or to others, verbosely.

For snakes fall out of trees, this is my final word
and don't forget when I say this all that you've heard,
a snake must fall down unless lodged in a cavity
because: 'Snakes, in this world, are subject to gravity.'

And now to the thanks, I should first thank my father
without whom and so forth and so on but then rather
I should first thank my mother to whom all I owe
and blah blah and etcetera and so on, ditto,

and then thanks must go to my dear darling wife
and to the Swiss Army for making the knife
and to makers of clipboards in all times and all places
without whom I could never and the makers of laces

to tie up your shoes and the Royal Society
who paid for my trip and prevented anxiety
and I bow to the Queen as all great men should
when they've been in the jungle pursuing the good
and extending the boundaries of what's understood
and I expect, in due course, to receive a knighthood.

A Sir or a Lord or an Earl would do fine,
a Dukehood's okay if she find's one in time.
Disinterested science brings little reward,
except for that thing that she does, with a sword.

Farming Wisdom

Whether the wether can weather the weather
or whether the weather will weather the wether,
whichever we(a)ther weathers whatever
some weathering's bound to go on
and that is the point,
yes, that is the point,
yes, that is the point of this song.